THE ★ALL-TIME★GRE
MILLION-SELLING ★

WISE PUBLICATIONS
part of The Music Sales Group
London / New York / Paris / Sydney / Copenhagen / Berlin / Madrid / Tokyo

Published by
Wise Publications
8/9 Frith Street, London, W1D 3JB, England.

Exclusive distributors:
Music Sales Limited
Distribution Centre, Newmarket Road,
Bury St Edmunds, Suffolk, IP33 3YB, England.

Music Sales Pty Limited
120 Rothschild Avenue, Rosebery, NSW 2018, Australia.

Order No. AM92338
ISBN 0-7119-4414-8

This book © Copyright 2005 Wise Publications,
a division of Music Sales Limited.

Cover designed by Fresh Lemon.

Printed in the United Kingdom.

www.musicsales.com

2 Become 1

Words & Music by Matt Rowe, Richard Stannard, Melanie Brown, Victoria Adams, Geri Halliwell, Emma Bunton & Melanie Chisholm

8

Verse 2:

Silly games that you were playing, empty words we both were saying,
Let's work it out boy, let's work it out boy.
Any deal that we endeavour, boys and girls feel good together,
Take it or leave it, take it or leave it.
Are you as good as I remember baby, get it on, get it on,
'Cause tonight is the night when two become one.

I need some love like I never needed love before, (wanna make love to ya baby.)
I had a little love, now I'm back for more, (wanna make love to ya baby.)
Set your spirit free, it's the only way to be.

Baby One More Time

Words & Music by Max Martin

some-thin' was-n't right here? Oh ba-by, ba-by, I should-n't have let____ you go.

____ And now you're out of sight, yeah. Show me how you want it

to be. Tell me ba-by, 'cos I need to know now, oh, be-cause___

my lone-li-ness is kill-in' me and___ I,_____ I must con-fess I

Verse 2:
Oh baby, baby
The reason I breathe is you
Boy you got me blinded.
Oh pretty baby
There's nothing that I wouldn't do
It's not the way I planned it.

Show me, how you want it to be *etc.*

Candle In The Wind

Words & Music by Elton John & Bernie Taupin

Good - bye Nor - ma Jean, ___ though I nev - er knew you at all ___ you had ___ the grace to

hold your - self ___ while those a - round ___ you crawled. They crawled out of the

wood - work, ___ and they whis - pered in - to ___ your brain, ___ they set you on a tread -

- mill ___ and they made you change your name. ___ And it

seems to me you lived your life ___ like a can - dle in ___ the wind. ___ Nev - er

know - ing ___ who to cling ___ to ___ when the rain ___ set in. ___ And I

16

would have liked — to have known — you but — I was just — a kid, — your can - dle had burned — out

long — be - fore — your leg - end ev - er did. —

2. Lone - li - ness was tough, — the tough - est role you ev - er played, Hol - ly - wood cre - at - ed a —

17

su - per star and pain was the price you paid. Ev - en when you died,

oh the press still hound - ed you, all the pa - pers had to say was that

Ma - ri - lyn was found in the nude. And it seems to me you

lived your life like a can - dle in the wind. Nev - er know - ing who to cling

18

3.Good-bye Nor-ma Jean,___ though I nev-er knew you at all___

___ you had___ the grace to hold your-self___ while those a-round___ you crawled.___

Good-bye Nor-ma Jean___ from the young man in the

twen-ty sec-ond row___ who sees you as some-thing more than sex-u-al,___ more than

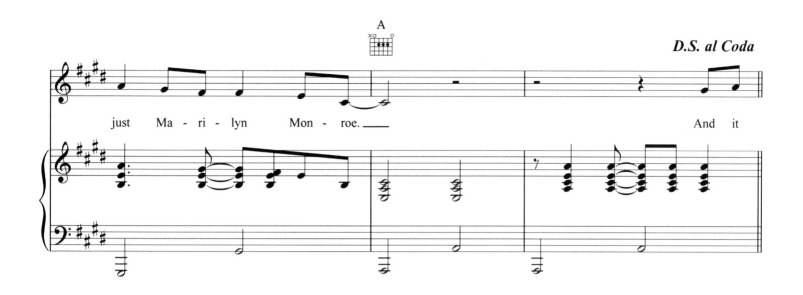

just Ma - ri - lyn Mon - roe.___ And it

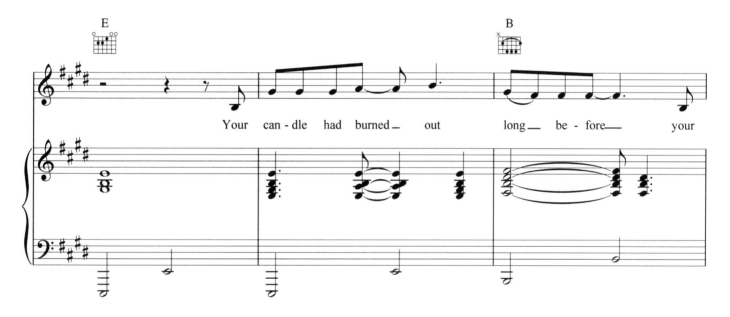

⊕ **Coda**

Your can - dle had burned_ out long_ be - fore_ your

leg - end ev - er did._____

Can't Get You Out Of My Head

Words & Music by Cathy Dennis & Rob Davis

23

Verse 2:
There's a dark secret in me
Don't leave me locked in your heart
Set me free *etc.*

Heart Of Glass

Words & Music by Deborah Harry & Chris Stein

Once I had a love_____ and it____ was a gas_____
Once I had a love_____ and it____ was a gas_____

soon turned out_____ had a heart of glass._____
soon turned out_____ to be a pain in the ass._____

Seemed like the real thing on - ly to find_____
Seemed like the real thing on - ly to find_____

mu - cho mis - trust, love's gone be - hind.____
mu - cho mis - trust, love's gone be - hind.____

To Coda

Once I had a love_____ and it was di - vine,____
Once I had a love_____ and it was a gas,____

soon found out I was los-ing my mind.
soon turned out had a heart of glass.

Seemed like the real thing but I___ was so blind,___
Seemed like the real thing but on-ly to find___

mu-cho mis-trust, love's gone be-hind.___
mu-cho mis-trust, love's gone be-hind.___

In be-tween___ what I find___ is pleas-ing and I'm feel-ing fine,___
Lost in time,___ a-do-ra-ble___ il-lu-sion and I can-not hide,___

La la la___ la la la la la la___ la la la la la la,___ la

la la la la la___ la la la la la la,___ la

la la la la la,___ yeah,___ rid - ing high on love's_ true_ blu-ish light.___

Ooh___ oh,___ ooh___ oh,___

ooh — oh, — ooh — oh.

Coda

E

Ooh — oh,

ooh — oh.

Repeat to fade

Careless Whisper

Words & Music by George Michael & Andrew Ridgeley

I feel so_____ un-sure_____
Time can nev-er mend
To-night the mu-sic seems so loud,_____ I

Don't Give Up On Us

Words & Music by Tony Macaulay

41

stars. We can't change___ ours. Don't give

up on us ba - by, we're still___ worth___ one more

try. I know we've put a last one___ by,___

just for a rain - y eve - ning when may - be stars are

Evergreen

Words & Music by Jorgen Elofsson, Per Magnusson & David Kreuger

look at me like that, what you're think-ing, what's be-hind._____ Don't tell_ me, but_ it

feels_____ like love._____ I'm gon-na take_ this mo-ment and make it last for-ev

-er._____ I'm gon-na give my heart_ a-way_ and pray_ we'll stay_ to-ge-

-ther. 'Cos you're the one good rea-son,_____ you're the on-ly girl

D
A
mo - ment and make it last for ev - er. I'm gon - na give my heart
G
Asus4
A
a - way and pray we'll stay to - ge - ther. 'Cos you're the one good
D
A
rea - son, you're the on - ly girl that I need; 'cos you're more
1.
G
Asus4
A
beau - ti - ful than I have ev - er seen. I'm gon - na take this

Verse 2:
Touch like an angel
Like velvet to my skin
And I wonder
I wonder why you wanna stay the night
What you're dreaming
What's behind.
Don't tell me, but it feels like love.

I'm gonna take this moment *etc.*

(Everything I Do) I Do It For You

Words by Bryan Adams & Robert John Lange
Music by Michael Kamen

1. Look in-to my eyes, you will see what you mean to me. Search your heart, search your
2. Look in-to your heart, you will find there's noth-ing there to hide. Take me as I am, take my

50

I Love You Love Me Love

Words & Music by Gary Glitter & Mike Leander

1. We're still to - geth - er af - ter all that we've been through.
2. The things they said a - bout the two of us were lies.

They tried to tell you I was not the boy for you. They
I knew they could - n't see the love - light in your eyes. They

did - n't like my hair, the clothes I love to wear. They
said I would - n't dare to show how much I care. They

did - n't re - al - ise that I was strong e - nough for two.
did - n't know that we were just two an - gels in dis - guise.

I Remember You

Words by Johnny Mercer
Music by Victor Schertzinger

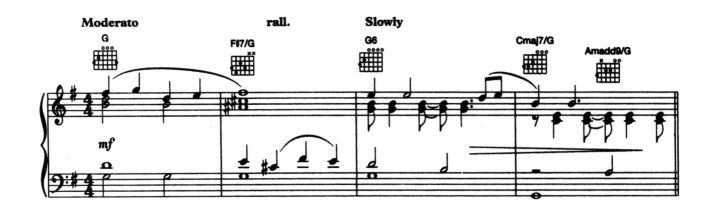

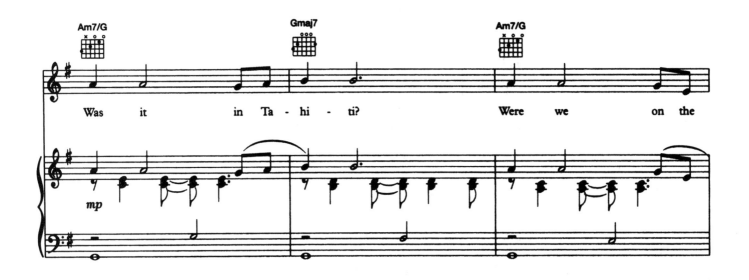

Was it in Ta-hi-ti? Were we on the

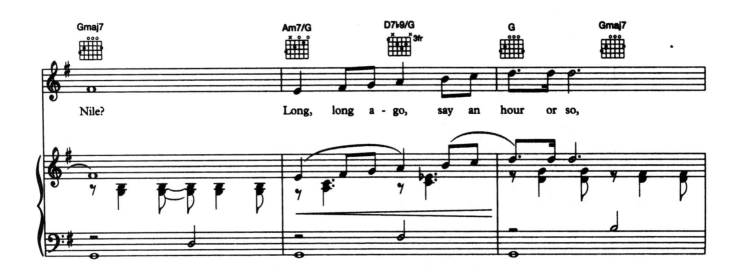

Nile? Long, long a-go, say an hour or so,

59

said, 'I love you too.' I do, did-n't you know?____

____ I re-mem-ber too, a dis-tant bell,

and stars that fell like rain, out of the

blue.____ When my life is

I Will Always Love You

Words & Music by Dolly Parton

Slow, freely

If___ I_____ should___ stay,_____ I___ would-

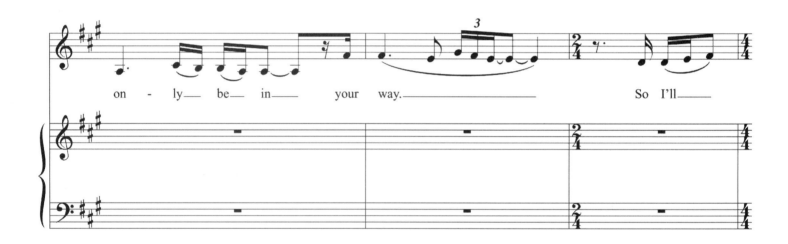

on - ly___ be___ in___ your way._____ So I'll___

go,_____ but I___ know___ I'll___

67

Imagine

Words & Music by John Lennon

Verse 2:
Imagine there's no countries
It isn't hard to do
Nothing to kill or die for
And no religion too
Imagine all the people living life in peace.

Verse 3:
Imagine no possessions
I wonder if you can
No need for greed or hunger
A brotherhood of man
Imagine all the people sharing all the world.

It's Now Or Never

Words & Music by Wally Gold, Aaron Schroeder & Eduardo Di Capua

my heart was cap - tured, my soul sur-

-ren - dered. I've spent a life - time wait - ing for the

right time. Now that you're near, the time is here at

last. It's now or nev - er, come hold me

tight. Kiss me my dar - ling, be mine to-

night. To - mor - row_____ will be too

late; it's now or nev - er, my love won't

wait. 2.Just like a It's now or nev - er,

Verse 2:
Just like a willow, we would cry an ocean
If we lost true love and sweet devotion.
Your lips excite me, let your arms invite me
For who knows when we'll meet again this way?

Karma Chameleon

**Words & Music by George O'Dowd, Jonathan Moss, Roy Hay,
Michael Craig & Philip Pickett**

78

81

Killing Me Softly With His Song

Words by Norman Gimbel
Music by Charles Fox

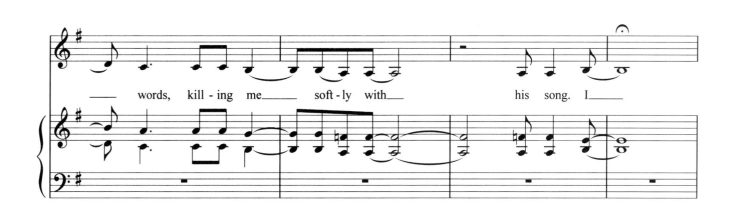

words, kill - ing me_____ soft - ly with_____ his song. I_____

N.C.

8 bars rhythm

1. heard he sang_____ a good_____ song, I

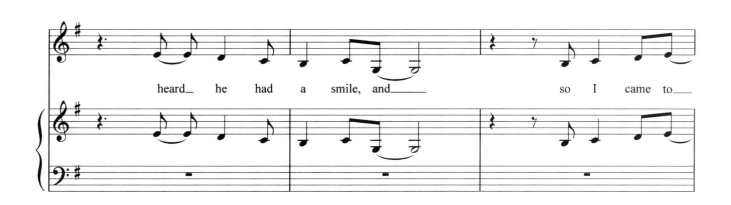

heard_____ he had a smile, and_____ so I came to_____

_____ see him_____ and lis - ten for_____ a while. _____

words, kill - ing me____ soft - ly____ with his song

Oh_____ oh_____

_____ la la la____ la la____ la woh__

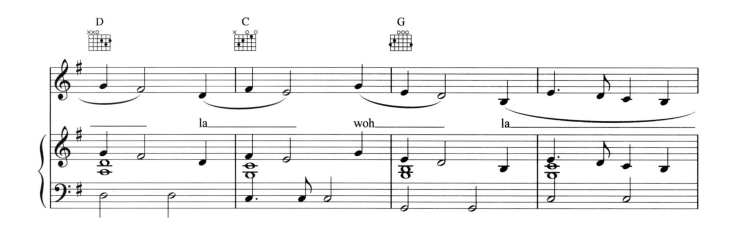

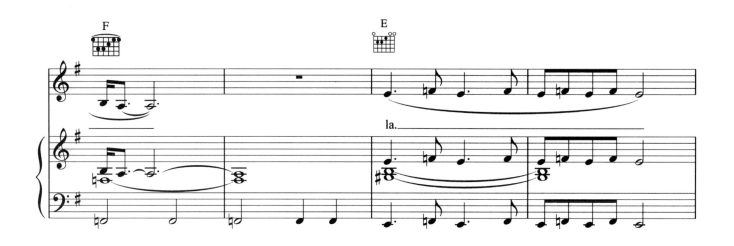

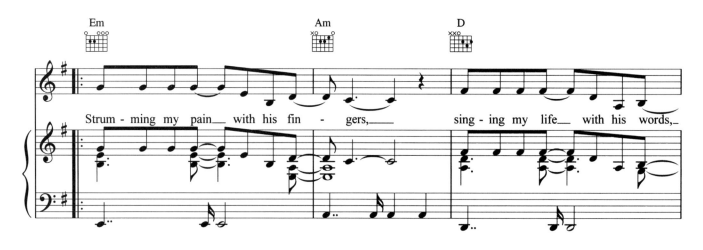

Verse 2:
I felt all flushed with fever,
Embarrassed by the crowd,
I felt he found my letters
And read each one out loud,
I prayed that he would finish
But he just kept right on...

Mull Of Kintyre

Words & Music by Paul McCartney & Denny Laine

mountains__ with valleys__ of green. Past paint-ed des-erts__ the

sun-set's on fire__ as he car - ries me home__ to the Mull__ of Kin -

tyre. Mull__ of Kin - tyre Oh mist roll-ing in from__ the

sea, my de-sire is al-ways to be here Oh Mull__ of Kin -

tyre.

Sweep through the heath-er like deer in the glen Car-ry me back to the days I knew then. Nights when we

My Heart Will Go On
(Love Theme From 'Titanic')

Words by Will Jennings. Music by James Horner

1. Ev - 'ry night in my dreams I see you, I
2. Love can touch us one time and last for a

Con pedale

Never Ever

Words & Music by Shaznay Lewis, Esmail Jazayeri & Sean Mather

or even on the phone, you can write it in a letter, either way I have to know. Did I never treat you right?

Did I always start the fight? Either way I'm going out of my mind, all the answers to my questions I have to find.

1. My head's spin - ning,
(Verse 2 see block lyric)
boy I'm in a daze,___ I feel i - so - lat - ed,___

don't want to com - mun - i - cate. I'll take a show - er, I will___ scour,___ I will run,___

99

Verse 2:
I keep searching deep within my soul
For all the answers, don't wanna hurt no more.
I need peace, got to feel at ease, need to be
Free from pain, go insane, my heart aches.

Sometimes vocabulary runs through my head
The alphabet runs from A to Z
Conversations, hesitations in my mind.
You got my conscience asking questions that I can't find
I'm not crazy
I'm sure I ain't done nothing wrong
Now I'm just waiting
'Cos I heard that this feeling won't last that long.

Love Is All Around

Words & Music by Reg Presley

1. I feel it in my fin-gers, I feel it in my toes.—
(Verse 2 see block lyric)

The love that's all a-round me

You know I love you, I al-ways— will,— my mind's made up by the

way that I feel.— There's no be-gin-ning, there'll be no— end,— 'cause

1.

on my— love— you can de-pend.—

2. I

106

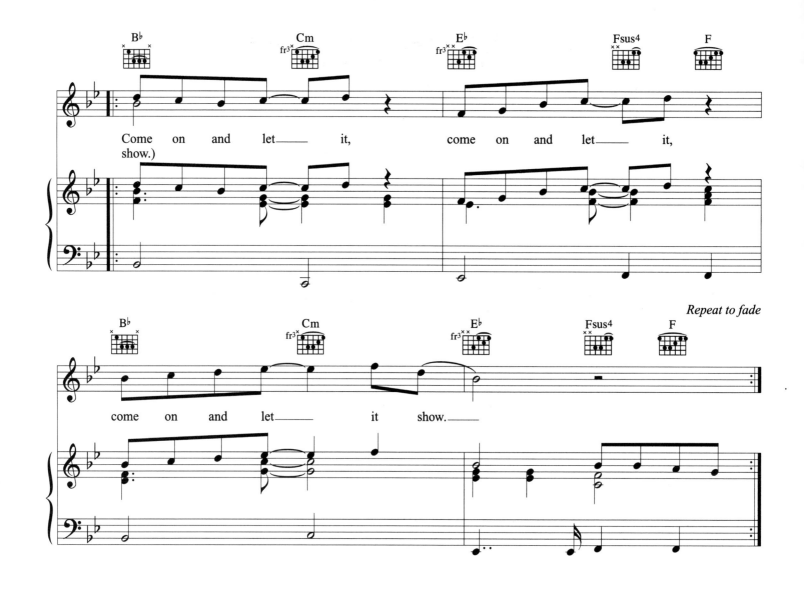

Repeat to fade

Come on and let—— it, come on and let—— it,
show.)

come on and let—— it show.——

Verse 2:
I see your face before me
As I lay on my bed;
I cannot get to thinking
Of all the things you said.
You gave your promise to me
And I gave mine to you;
I need someone beside me
In everything I do.

No Matter What

Music by Andrew Lloyd Webber
Lyrics by Jim Steinman

No mat-ter what they tell us, no mat-ter what they do,
If on-ly tears were laugh-ter, if on-ly night was day,

no mat-ter what they teach us, what we be-lieve is true.
if on-ly prayers were an-swered then we would hear God say.

I know our love's for - ev - er,
No mat - ter where it's bar - ren

I know no mat - ter what.
our dream is be - ing born.

f Instrumental

No mat-ter who they fol-low, no mat-ter where they lead,

no mat-ter how they judge us I'll be eve-ry one you need.

No mat-ter if___ the sun___ don't shine,___

or if the___ skies are blue.___ No mat-ter what the

Pure And Simple

Words & Music by Tim Hawes, Pete Kirtley & Alison Clarkson

116

Verse 2:
I'll be there through the stormiest weather
Always trying to make things a bit better
And I know I gotta try and get through to you
You can love me in a way like no other
But the situation's taking you under
So you need to tell me now what you wanna do.

I know I've been walking around in a daze (Baby, baby)
You gotta believe me when I say (Ah, ooh, ooh)

Wherever you go *etc.*

Tragedy

Words & Music by Barry Gibb, Maurice Gibb & Robin Gibb

Here I lie in a lost and lone - ly part of town,
Night and day there's a burn - ing down in - side of me.

held in time in a world of tears I slow - ly drown.
Burn - ing love with a yearn - ing tears that won't let me be.

F

Go - in' home I just can't make it all a - lone, I
Down I go and I just can't take it all a - lone, I

G

F

real - ly should be hold - ing you, hold - ing you,
real - ly should be hold - ing you, hold - ing you,

Ab

lov - ing you, lov - ing you.
lov - ing you, lov - ing you.

Trag - e - dy, ___ when the feel - ing's gone and you can't go on, it's

trag - e - dy; ___ when the morn - ing cries and you don't know why, it's

hard to bear ___ with no one to love you you're go - in' no - where.

Trag - e - dy, ___ when you lose con - trol and you got no soul, it's

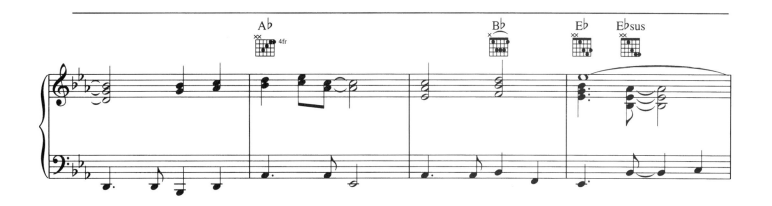

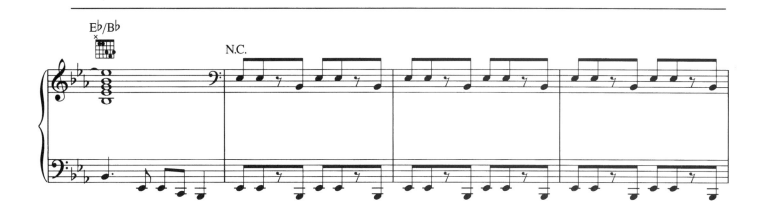

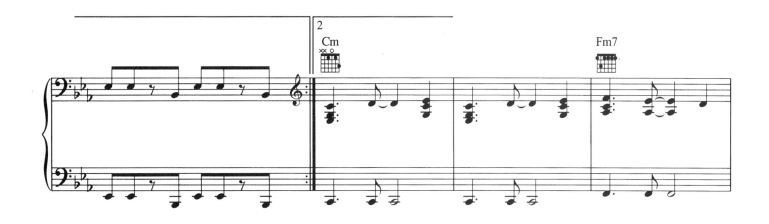

Trag - e - dy,___ when the feel - ing's gone and you can't go on, it's

trag - e - dy;___ when the morn - ing cries and you don't know why, it's

hard to bear___ with no one to love you, you're go - in' no - where.

Trag - e - dy, ___ when you lose con - trol and you got no soul, it's

trag - e - dy; ___ when the morn - ing cries and your heart just dies, it's

hard to bear ___ with no one to love you you're

go - in' no - where. Oh. ___

Repeat and Fade

125

Relax

Words & Music by Peter Gill, Holly Johnson & Mark O'Toole

When you wan - na come.____

Em

Em⁷

(ad lib. vocal)

When you wan - na come._ Come!

Huh! *(ad lib. vocal)*

Re - lax, don't do it

Release Me

Words & Music by Eddie Miller, Dub Williams & Robert Yount

Moderato, with feeling

Please re - lease me, let me go _____ For
I have found a new love, dear, _____ And
Please re - lease me, can't you see _____ You'd

I don't love you an - y - more. To
I will al - ways want her near. Her
be a fool to cling to me. To

Rivers Of Babylon

Words & Music by Frank Farian, George Reyam, Brent Dowe & James McNaughton

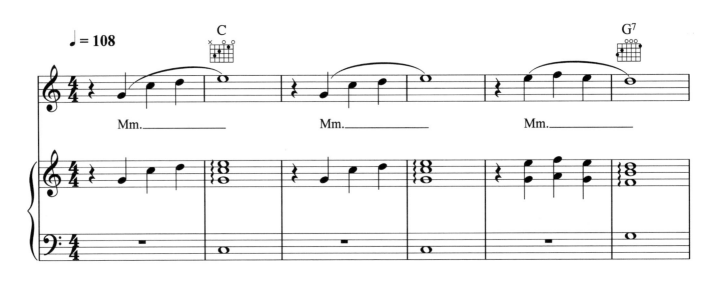

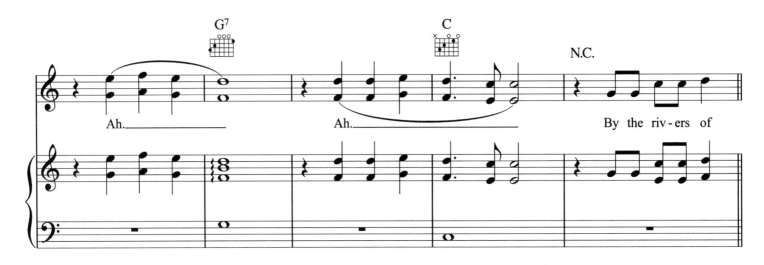

land?　　　　　　　　Mm.　　　　　　　　　　　　Mm.

Mm.　　　　　　　　　　Mm.

Let the words　　of our mouths　　and＿ the me-di-

-ta - tion of our hearts　be ac - cep - ta-ble in thy sight here to-

night. Let the words of our mouths and the me-di-

-ta-tion of our hearts be ac-cep-ta-ble in thy

sight here to-night. By the riv-ers of

D.S. al Coda

Coda

Vocals 2° only ____

Ah. ____

Rock Around The Clock

Words & Music by Max C. Freedman & Jimmy De Knight

One, two, three o'-clock, four o'-clock rock, five, six, sev-en o'-clock, eight o' clock rock.

Nine, ten, e-le-ven o'-clock, twelve o' clock rock, we're gon-na rock a-round the clock to-night. Put your

glad rags on and join me, Hon,_ we'll have some fun when the clock strikes one,_ we're gon-na
(Verse 2 -5 see block lyric)

rock a - round the clock to - night,__ we're gon - na rock, rock, rock, 'til broad day - light,__ we're gon - na

rock, gon - na rock a - round__ the clock_ to - night._____ 2. When the

Verse 2:
When the clock strikes two and three and four
If the band slows down we'll yell for more.
We're gonna rock around the clock tonight
We're gonna rock, rock, rock 'til broad daylight
We're gonna rock, gonna rock around the clock tonight.

Verse 3:
When the chimes ring five and six and seven
We'll be rockin' up in seventh heav'n.
We're gonna rock around the clock tonight
We're gonna rock, rock, rock 'til broad daylight
We're gonna rock, gonna rock around the clock tonight.

Verse 4:
When it's eight, nine, ten, eleven, too
I'll be goin' strong and so will you.
We're gonna rock around the clock tonight
We're gonna rock, rock, rock 'til broad daylight
We're gonna rock, gonna rock around the clock tonight.

Verse 5:
When the clock strikes twelve, we'll cool off, then
Start a rockin' 'round the clock again.
We're gonna rock around the clock tonight
We're gonna rock, rock, rock 'til broad daylight
We're gonna rock, gonna rock around the clock tonight.

She Loves You

Words & Music by John Lennon & Paul McCartney

Moderately ♩ = 100

She loves you, yeah, yeah, yeah.___ She loves you, yeah,

yeah, yeah.___ She loves you, yeah, yeah, yeah, yeah.___

1. You think you've lost your love?___ Well, I saw her yes - ter -
(2.) said you hurt her so,___ she al - most lost her
(3.) know it's up to you,___ I think it's on - ly

mf

day._____ It's you she's think - ing of_____ and she told me what to
mind,_____ and now she says she knows_____ you're not the hurt - ing
fair,_____ pride can hurt you too,_____ a - pol - o - gize to

say:_____ she says she
kind._____ She says she loves you and you know that can't be
her._____ Be - cause she

bad. Yes, she loves you and you know you should be glad.

Tainted Love

Words & Music by Ed Cobb

With a moving beat

Unchained Melody

Words by Hy Zaret
Music by Alex North

mine? _____ I need your love, _____ I need your love, _____

God speed your love _____ to me! _____

1. Lone - ly riv - ers flow _____ to the sea, _____ to the sea,
2. Lone - ly moun - tains gaze _____ at the stars, _____ at the stars,

To the o - pen arms _____ of the sea. _____
Wait - ing for the dawn _____ of the day. _____

You're The One That I Want

Words & Music by John Farrar

it's e-lec-tri-fy-in'!

(2.) (Feel your way)

C

Em

You bet-ter shape up, 'cause I need a man,

Am

F

and my heart is set on you.

C

You bet-ter shape up, you bet-ter un-

Verse 2:

If you're filled with affection you're too shy to convey
Meditate in my direction, feel your way.

I better shape up 'cause you need a man
Who can keep you satisfied.
I better shape up if I'm gonna prove
That your faith is justified.

(Are you sure?
Yes I'm sure down deep inside.)

You're the one *etc.*

123456789

Bringing you the words and the music

All the latest music in print... rock & pop plus jazz, blues, country, classical and the best in West End show scores.

- Books to match your favourite CDs.

- Book-and-CD titles with high quality backing tracks for you to play along to. Now you can play guitar or piano with your favourite artist... or simply sing along!

- Audition songbooks with CD backing tracks for both male and female singers for all those with stars in their eyes.

- Can't read music? No problem, you can still play all the hits with our wide range of chord songbooks.

- Check out our range of instrumental tutorial titles, taking you from novice to expert in no time at all!

- Musical show scores include *The Phantom Of The Opera*, *Les Misérables*, *Mamma Mia* and many more hit productions.

- DVD master classes featuring the techniques of top artists.